— *Dedications* —

For my dear husband, Jay, with love and gratitude
for his unending encouragement and support.

And for my children—Holly, Miles, and Crystal—
who continue to fill my life with joy.

Pearl

ISLAND HERITAGE™
PUBLISHING
A DIVISION OF THE MADDEN CORPORATION

94-411 Kō'aki Street, Waipahu, Hawai'i 96797-2806
Orders: (800) 468-2800
Information: (808) 564-8800
Fax: (808) 564-8877
islandheritage.com

ISBN NO. 1-59700-099-X
First Edition, Third Printing — 2007

My Hawaiian Farm

Written by Pearl Maxner
Illustrated by Pearl Maxner
and Anneth Lagamo

ISLAND HERITAGE™
PUBLISHING

Every month of the year exciting things are happening on my Hawaiian farm.

In January my *'ohana* is picking limes for the juice factory.

I help the chickens find bugs under the rocks. Watch out for Mr. Mongoose, he likes eggs too!

February finds the wild pigs rooting in the orchards at night. Uncle will bring one home for *lūʻau* soon. I pick a cherimoya. So sweet and fruity, I want to eat them all!

March is showing off with lemons, tangerines, and oranges on the trees. So many birds are building their nests. The 'io is excited as he looks for mice running away from the tractor mower.

8

April's rains have caused the tree ferns to unfurl new fronds in the forest. I run to my secret place there and find the Chinese orchid in bloom. I am careful not to disturb the shearwater nesting under the *uluhe* fern. It is the biggest secret of all.

In May we eat papayas every morning for breakfast. Pineapples too! Tūtū harvests eggplants, breadfruit, sweet potatoes, and bok choy for stew. Taro has been made into poi for baby Keawe's *lū'au* tonight.

11

I love to stick my nose in the fragrant rose apple blossoms in June. Up in their branches the *liliko'i* twines. Higher still I see the *'apapane* come in big flocks in the morning light. At the end of a day of feasting on *'ōhi'a lehua* blossoms, they will go back up the slopes of Mauna Loa to sleep.

13

14

July's hot sun feels good on my back as I pick the yellow guavas. Lettuce and tomatoes for the salad, herbs for Mama, kale for greens, rhubarb for pie...did I forget anything?

In August I watch my brother chopping the banana stalk. Slow now, don't let it crash! We pick green beans, limas, and pull up big carrots. They will all be sold at the fruit stand in town.

17

Sometimes on warm nights in September Papa takes me "slugging." We wear our headlamps and fill our buckets with snails and slugs. The ducks will be happy to eat them in the morning. Mrs. Rat shares in the hunt.

19

October is a month of picking macadamia nuts. We all pick and pick. The bags stack up in the trucks. The sheep are mowing the grass so we can find the nuts. Will we ever be done?

21

November's harvest of avocados is my favorite. The buckets fill up fast. Everyone smiles, even Tūtū Kane. Sandy, our dog, loves avocados too. I am glad the centipedes are asleep now.

22

December's storms bring warmth from the cookstove. Time to repair the tools, dance, and sing. Papa plays the steel guitar, and I fall asleep.

25

The world is at peace on my Hawaiian farm.